STAR WARS REBELS™

COLOURING
ACTIVITY BOOK

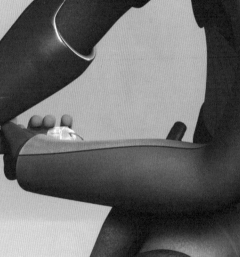

EGMONT

We bring stories to life

First published in Great Britain 2014
by Egmont UK Limited, The Yellow Building,
1 Nicholas Road, London W11 4AN.

ISBN 978 1 4052 7641 2
59650/1
Printed in Italy

LOTHAL LONER

Ezra is an orphan who lives on the streets of Lothal. He hates the Empire, so when the chance comes to join forces with the rebels, he is more than happy to leave his street-rat life behind. Colour in the newest member of the *Ghost* crew.

EZRA

Age: **15**

Species: **Human**

Homeworld: **Lothal**

Special skills: **Quick, clever, amazing thief and con artist, excellent reflexes, escape and infiltration skills**

Signature equipment: **Wrist-mounted energy slingshot and stolen Imperial helmet collection**

Likes: **Playing pranks on Chopper**

Dislikes: **Zeb's complaining**

SECRET JEDI

Kanan is the commander of the *Ghost* gang.
He is also a Jedi Knight, one of the few to survive Order 66.
Colour in this lightsaber-wielding leader.

KANAN

Age: **27**

Species: **Human**

Homeworld: **Coruscant**

Special skills: **Jedi capabilities, excellent leader, cunning strategist**

Signature equipment: **Lightsaber and gunslinger blaster**

Likes: **Planning missions to take down the Empire**

Dislikes: **Being told how to shoot**

TOP TWI'LEK

Hera is the owner and pilot of the *Ghost*. She is an excellent flyer, and also keeps the rest of her crewmates focused and united. Don't mess with this tough Twi'lek – but do colour her in!

HERA

Age: **24**

Species: **Twi'lek**

Homeworld: **Ryloth**

Special skills: **Ace pilot, skilled shooter, making connections**

Signature equipment: ***Ghost***

Likes: **Being in the cockpit**

Dislikes: **When the *Ghost* is damaged**

MIGHTY MUSCLE

If Kanan is the brains of the group then Zeb is the brawn. This loud Lasat is always up for a brawl with Imperials. Colour in Zeb in his fighting pose.

ZEB

Age: **39**

Species: **Lasat**

Homeworld: **Lasan**

Special skills: **Hand-to-hand combat, heightened strength and stamina**

Signature equipment: **Bo-rifle – combination fighting staff and laser rifle, the traditional weapon of the Honour Guard of Lasat**

Likes: **Punching stormtroopers**

Dislikes: **His number one enemy, Agent Kallus**

WHICH REBEL ARE YOU?

Answer these questions to find out which *Ghost* crew member you are most like.

1. WHAT IS YOUR FAVOURITE PASTIME?

a) Fighting

b) Flying

c) Fixing things

d) Painting

2. HOW WOULD YOUR FRIENDS DESCRIBE YOUR PERSONALITY?

a) Fearless and loyal

b) Protective and clever

c) Grumpy and sarcastic

d) Creative and daring

3. WHICH WEAPON WOULD YOU CHOOSE?

a) Bo-rifle

b) The *Ghost*

c) *Phantom*

d) Explosives

5. IF YOU SEE A GROUP OF STORMTROOPERS WHAT DO YOU DO?

a) Attack

b) Call for back-up

c) Run away

d) Play a prank on them

4. WHAT IS YOUR ULTIMATE DREAM?

a) To protect people

b) To own your own starship

c) To be appreciated by your friends

d) To create a masterpiece

ANSWERS:

Mostly As: You are like Zeb. You don't think before you act and often get yourself into trouble, but your heart is in the right place. You would never let anyone hurt your friends.

Mostly Bs: You are like Hera. You are the peacemaker amongst your friends. People always ask you for advice because you are trustworthy and wise.

Mostly Cs: You are like Chopper. You can be a bit moody, but you are there when your friends need you. You provide comic relief to any stressful situation.

Mostly Ds: You are like Sabine. You are wild and creative, and can always be counted on to put together a scheme!

MY SPECIAL TALENT IS: _____

REBEL STYLE

Join the band of rebels by drawing yourself in flight gear. Don't forget a weapon and decide what your special talent will be.

MESSY MISSION

Your first mission as member of the *Ghost* crew is to cause some havoc to the stormtroopers. Graffiti their armour with your favourite colours and make up some rebel symbols.

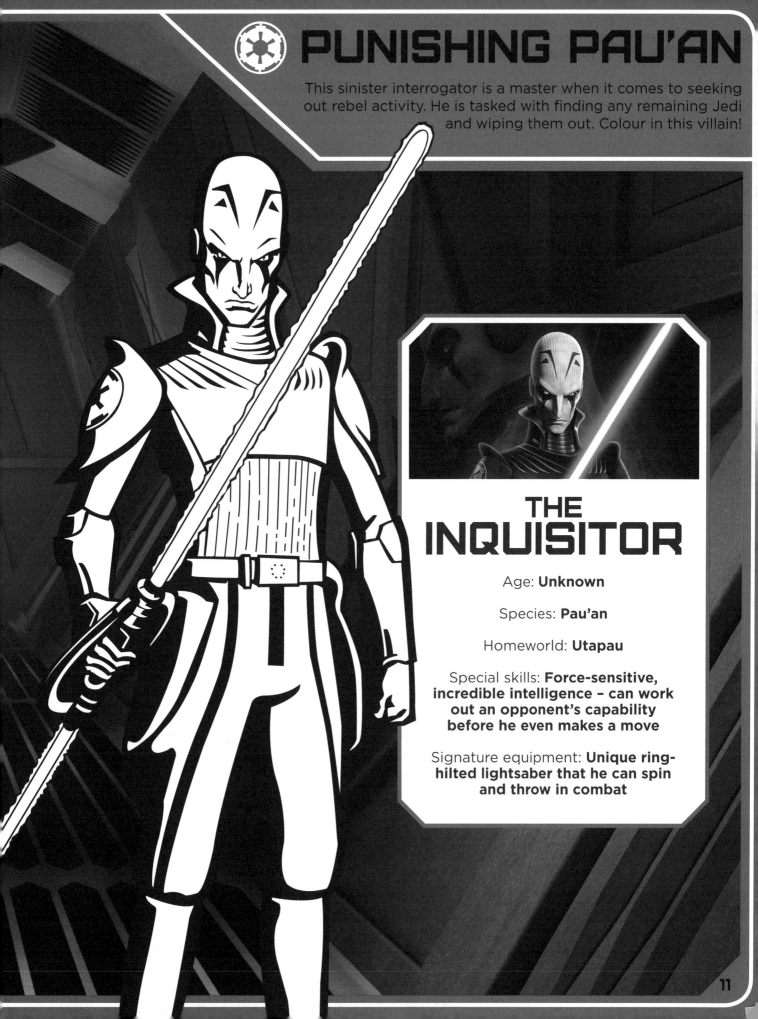

PUNISHING PAU'AN

This sinister interrogator is a master when it comes to seeking out rebel activity. He is tasked with finding any remaining Jedi and wiping them out. Colour in this villain!

THE INQUISITOR

Age: **Unknown**

Species: **Pau'an**

Homeworld: **Utapau**

Special skills: **Force-sensitive, incredible intelligence – can work out an opponent's capability before he even makes a move**

Signature equipment: **Unique ring-hilted lightsaber that he can spin and throw in combat**

MISCHIEVOUS MACHINE

Chopper is well known for his cheeky attitude and pranks on his fellow crewmates. But he is a vital part of the group and the *Ghost* wouldn't work without him. Colour in this grumpy droid.

CHOPPER

Age: **Very old**

Species: **Astromech Droid**

Homeworld: **Unknown, acquired used**

Special skills: **Starship repair, astrogation**

Signature equipment: **Booster rocket, computer probe**

Likes: **Playing pranks on Ezra**

Dislikes: **Almost everything**

BOMB BUILDER

Sabine is a Mandalorian with a special talent for explosives. When she isn't trying to blow up Imperial ships she's tagging them with her unique graffiti. Colour in this super soldier.

SABINE

Age: **16**

Species: **Human**

Homeworld: **Mandalore**

Special skills: **Explosives expert, street artist**

Signature equipment: **Art supplies, handmade explosives, Mandalorian helmet**

Likes: **Customising her possessions, tagging Imperial ships**

Dislikes: **Authority**

SKY WARRIOR

The *Ghost* is the ship where the rebels live, plan missions and fight TIE fighters. It tangles with TIE fighters a lot, but luckily Chopper keeps it in top shape. Give the *Ghost* a new paint job.

DORSAL LASER CANNON TURRET

COCKPIT

THE GHOST

MAIN ION ENGINES (3)

MY SHIP IS CALLED: _____

STARSHIP WORKSHOP

If you were to form your own band of rebels, you would need a ship for home base and flying missions. Design your own starship here.

Copy the colours to create masterpieces of these rebel heroes!

HERO SEARCH

Find all the rebels and their ships in this wordsearch.

R	E	U	W	L	T	T	C	P	A	G	U	T	J	Z
K	A	E	S	F	C	Q	F	R	H	D	S	W	G	B
O	A	P	F	U	L	H	Z	H	X	K	P	Z	X	I
F	A	N	D	U	E	E	O	S	U	U	A	R	E	H
I	F	R	A	S	I	A	Y	P	U	C	L	W	Q	J
M	E	A	P	N	I	M	H	P	P	B	F	R	F	K
G	J	X	O	R	U	A	X	M	B	E	P	U	J	I
Y	Q	H	Y	E	N	I	B	A	S	Z	R	I	S	W
A	K	Y	X	T	E	P	T	K	C	T	U	A	E	E
G	L	I	O	R	H	U	N	V	Q	J	A	E	L	X
L	U	M	Y	D	S	A	X	L	B	A	G	Q	O	N
B	I	S	E	Y	C	X	M	M	F	G	Z	V	E	I
H	I	K	W	C	Q	N	I	S	Z	C	J	B	U	L
D	K	O	H	C	O	P	N	T	S	O	H	G	G	P
Y	M	Q	M	T	S	B	Q	M	U	Z	Y	X	M	A

| EZRA | HERA | ZEB | GHOST |
| KANAN | SABINE | CHOPPER | PHANTOM |

BACK-UP BATTLESHIP

The *Phantom* is a secondary ship docked in the *Ghost*. It has a single-seat cockpit, and is perfect for short range fighting missions. Brighten up the *Phantom* with your colouring pencils.

LASER CANNONS

PHANTOM

COCKPIT

MAIN ION ENGINES (2)

SPACE BATTLE

The *Ghost* is returning home after another mission disrupting the Empire, but there are Imperial fighters on their tail. Colour in the *Ghost* and the ships chasing them.

COMMANDER COPY

Ezra loves to collect Imperial helmets as trophies.
Draw this stormtrooper helmet using the grid to help you.

REBEL MASTERPIECE

Sabine has sneaked into an Imperial hangar to wreak some colourful havoc with her graffiti kit. Help her out by colouring in this enemy ship and adding some rebel propaganda!

SHADOW SHIPS

Star Destroyers are above Lothal, reminding the citizens of the Empire's presence. Which shadow matches this mighty vessel?

MIRROR MENACE

Complete this picture of the Inquisitor by mirroring the first half.

EMPIRE ART

Copy the colours to create an amazing picture of the evil Inquisitor!

MY VILLAIN'S NAME IS:

NEW RECRUIT

The Empire is always looking for new recruits to join its fight against the rebels. Design your own Imperial villain here. Will he have a double lightsaber like the Inquisitor? Or a blaster like the stormtroopers?

DROID WORKSHOP

Chopper is an astromech droid, designed to fix ships, but there are many different types of droids in the *Star Wars* universe. You and your friends can draw your own unique droid by following these instructions.

1.

Everyone needs a piece of paper and a pen. Each person draws a droid head on their piece of paper.

2.

Then everyone passes their paper to someone else, and adds a shape for the droid's body on their new piece of paper.

3.

Everyone keeps passing on their paper, adding something new each time.

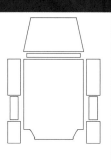
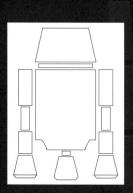
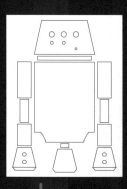

AT THE END, EVERYONE SHARES THEIR FINAL PICTURES.

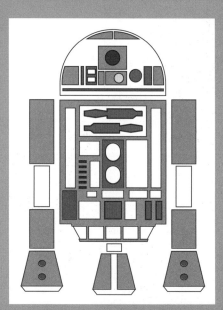

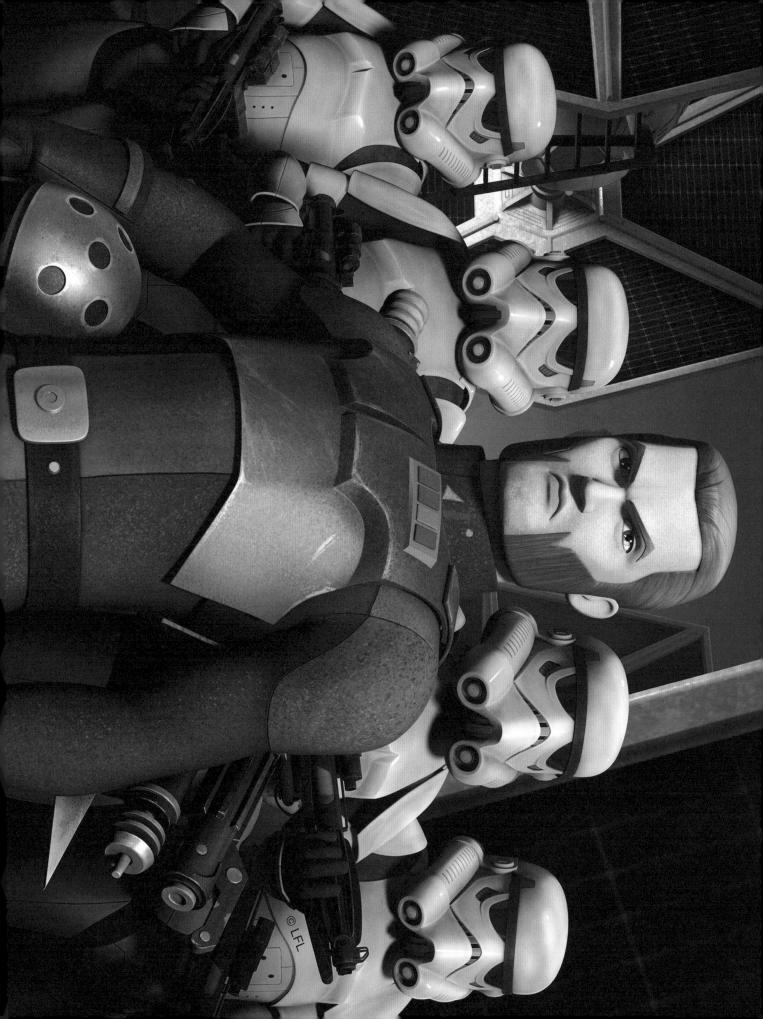

DARING DASH

Kanan and Zeb have been separated from each other and the *Ghost*. Can you get Kanan to the ship and then fly by to pick up Zeb? Colour in these rebels and the *Ghost* when you are done.

KANAN

START

FINISH

ZEB

MENACING MUDDLES

The rebel gang has a lot of enemies amongst the Empire.
Unscramble the name of some the more notorious villains on Lothal.

1. QINSIUOITR

2. TPSOROOTRMRSE

3. GTAEN LULSKA

4. NGIRT

5. RAKOSE

IMPERIAL IMPOSTER

The troopers are on patrol, but there is a stranger in their midst. Which stormtrooper is not like the others? When you have found him, graffiti these soldiers of the Empire with your colouring pencils.

LOTHAL SHOWDOWN

The Imperials have found the rebels on Lothal. The fight begins!
Colour in this exciting battle scene.

IMPERIAL FLEET

TIE fighters are easily recognisable by the roar of their engines. The pilots of these intimidating vessels are known as the dominant warriors of the sky and not to be messed with. Colour in this mighty machine.

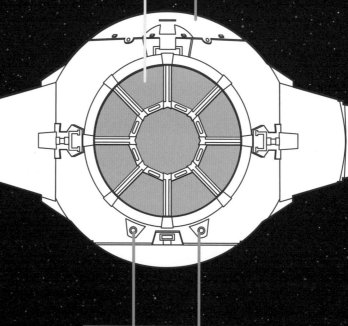

COCKPIT ACCESS HATCH

MAIN VIEWPORT

LASER CANNONS

TIE FIGHTER

BOY WONDER

Ezra is special, and only Kanan can see why. Can you spot five differences between these two pictures?

IMPERIAL SPY

The Empire is spying on the rebels but their lenses are too zoomed in. Can you work out which rebel is in each picture?

1

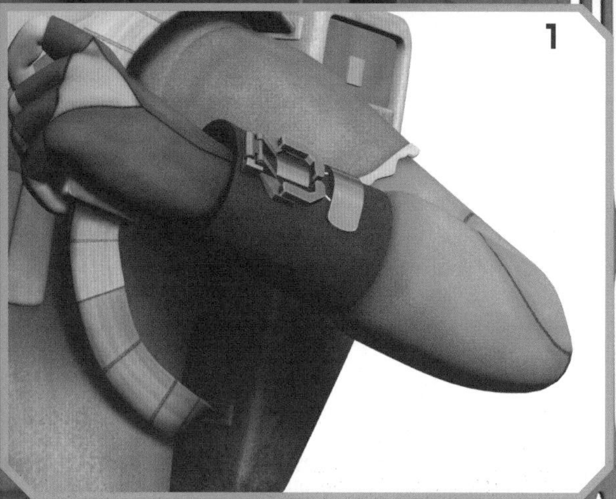

2

3

4

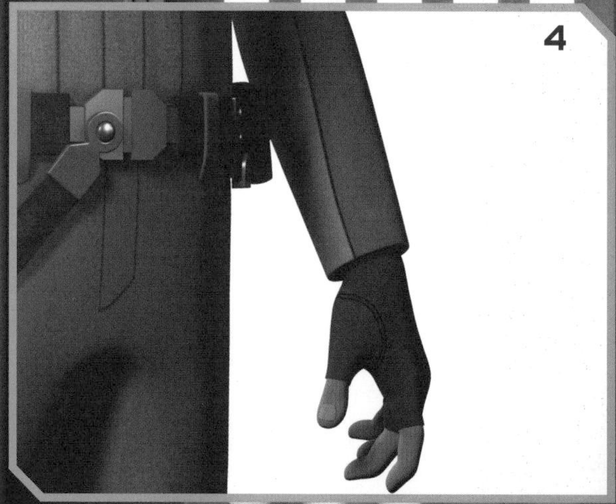

5

6

PICTURE PUZZLER

Complete the grid below so that all six rebels appear in every row, column and outlined 6-square block.

HERA			ZEB		SABINE
	SABINE			KANAN	
CHOPPER					EZRA
EZRA					HERA
	HERA			SABINE	
SABINE	ZEB				KANAN

WORD WARRIOR

How many words can you make from the phrase
"Stormtroopers on patrol"?
You can only use each letter once in each word.

HERE ARE A FEW TO GET YOU STARTED:

PEARL

POST

PETROL

CHOPPER COPY

Chopper is a valuable member of the *Ghost* crew, even if he doesn't get treated like it! Draw Chopper using the grid as a guide.

IMPERIAL SPY

Kanan and Zeb have just rescued some prisoners from Imperial headquarters on Lothal, but now the Inquisitor is hot on their tail. Colour in this great chase!

ANSWERS

Page 18 HERO SEARCH:

R	E	V	W	L	T	T	C	P	A	G	U	T	J	Z
A	A	E	S	F	C	Q	F	A	H	D	S	W	G	B
O	A	P	F	V	L	H	Z	H	X	K	P	Z	X	I
F	A	N	D	U	E	E	O	S	U	V	A	R	E	H
I	F	R	A	S	I	A	Y	P	U	C	L	W	Q	J
M	E	A	P	N	I	M	H	P	A	B	F	R	F	K
G	J	X	O	R	U	A	X	M	B	E	P	U	J	I
Y	Q	H	Y	E	N	I	B	A	S	Z	A	I	S	W
A	K	Y	X	T	E	P	T	K	C	T	U	A	E	E
G	L	I	O	R	H	U	N	V	Q	J	A	E	L	X
L	U	M	Y	D	S	A	X	L	B	A	G	Q	O	N
B	I	S	E	Y	C	X	M	M	F	G	Z	V	E	I
H	I	K	W	C	Q	N	I	S	Z	C	J	B	U	L
D	K	O	H	C	O	P	N	T	S	O	H	G	G	P
Y	M	Q	M	T	S	B	Q	M	U	Z	Y	X	M	A

Page 26 SHADOW SHIPS:
Shadow 4.

Page 33 DARING DASH:

START

FINISH

Page 34 MENACING MUDDLES:
1. INQUISITOR
2. STORMTROOPERS
3. AGENT KALLUS
4. GRINT
5. ARESKO

Page 35 IMPERIAL IMPOSTER:

Page 39 BOY WONDER:

Page 40 IMPERIAL SPY:
1. Ezra
2. Hera
3. Sabine
4. Kanan
5. Zeb
6. Chopper

Page 41 PICTURE PUZZLER: